Worrying W

Susannah McFarlane   Lachlan Creagh

A Scholastic Australia Book

This is Will and some of his friends—

Wyatt, Willow, Wes and Whitney.

Will is a worry wombat. He is probably one of the most worrisome wombats in the whole west. When he worries he wobbles and gets lots of worry wrinkles.

Will worries about the water tanks.
What if there won't be enough water
for the waratahs and the wattles?

Will worries about what he should wear
on the weekend.

What would be most winning—a woolly waistcoat or a white windcheater?

Will worries about the wayward
wheel on his wheelbarrow.
Would it wriggle right off and whirl
through the window?

And the more Will worries,
the more his wrinkles and
wobbles worsen.

Poor Will!

Then one day, one windy Wednesday, his friends decided they had to help Will work on his worries.

Willow showed him where all the wells were (and they watched the witchetty grubs water skiing).

When Will saw all that water
he thought he could worry
a wee bit less.

Wyatt said, 'Why not wear
the woolly waistcoat
AND the white windcheater?'

Will looked **wonderful!**

Wes warbled *Waltzing Matilda* and welded Will's wonky wheelbarrow.

And Whitney whistled along while working on Will's wrinkles.

It was working! Will was waving
away his woes.

Then the wobbles and wrinkles
began to whoosh away too!

What wonderful friends!

Good on you Will (and Wyatt,
Willow, Whitney and Wes).

What about you?
Do you work out your worries
sometimes too?